Don Law Golf Academy

Skills Improvement Workbook

By Rick Heard, PGA
Don Law, PGA

This Workbook Belongs To:

_____

Date: _____

Visit our website at www.donlawgolfacademy.com

Published by ARD Publishing
Boca Raton, Florida

Printed in the United States of America

CONTENTS

CONTENTS

INTRODUCTION

As golfers, we are constantly trying to lower our scores. In fact, the satisfaction that comes with improving our game may be one of the greatest joys of golf. The ongoing challenge to control our bodies and therefore control our golf ball is what keeps us coming back to the putting green, the range, and the golf course time after time. There are no short cuts, and improvement requires dedication and practice. When you decide to get serious and really strive to improve, you need to ensure you are practicing the right things. This Skills Improvement Workbook can help show you the way.

The game of golf has so many facets and nuances that it is almost impossible to be equally sharp in all areas. Besides pure ball striking abilities, there are full swings, partial swings, short game, bunker play, putting, and handling tough weather conditions – not to mention the internal challenges of strategic thinking, emotional control, and knowledge of the rules. Ultimately, it all comes down to ball control. This workbook focuses on ball control skills in all scoring areas, including putting, chipping, pitching, bunkers, approach shots, and trouble shots.

Whether you are a beginner or a scratch golfer, some areas of your game will always be stronger than others. Even the best PGA and LPGA Tour players are always working to improve. If you want to play to the best of your ability, you should too. There are three steps involved in making meaningful improvement in your golf skills:

1. Collect information on your current performance through a skills evaluation;

2. Analyze your results to identify improvement opportunities; and

3. Practice with a purpose.

Let's look at each of these steps in more detail.

Evaluate Your Current Skills

The first step on the road to improvement is to find out where you are right now. But how do you know where you are and where your improvement opportunities lie? To paraphrase the great physicist Lord Kelvin, "you can't improve what you can't measure," and it is true. You need a way to measure your current skill level so that you can determine which skills need the most improvement. And, in order to measure your skills, you need information. That information comes from a skills evaluation.

We have developed a series of Skills Assessment Worksheets that can help assess your strengths and improvement opportunities across all areas of your game. These worksheets provide detailed data that can be used to develop a comprehensive improvement plan for those who want to make a significant improvement in their scores.

Done properly, a skills evaluation will provide a measurement of the status of your game at a point in time. A proper evaluation will provide information that can be used to identify those high priority areas that have the greatest impact on lowering your scores. Repeated evaluations taken over time will show trends in your skills – hopefully becoming better and better!

There are two ways to evaluate your skills:

1. Conduct periodic skills evaluations using a standard skills assessment format, and

2. Record your performance statistics during tournament or serious rounds of golf where you play by USGA rules.

This workbook contains skills evaluation forms and a performance statistics scorecard that will help you collect information on nearly every area of your game. This information can then be analyzed to help develop a plan for productive practice.

Identify Improvement Opportunities

The second step on the road to improvement is to decide where you want to go. Once you have the information from the first step above, you can analyze it and truly understand your current strengths and weaknesses – let's call them "improvement opportunities."

The goal of your skills analysis should be to identify the highest priority improvement opportunities that will have the biggest impact on lowering your scores. Sometimes these areas will be obvious; other times it may be difficult to decide where you can get the biggest bang for the buck. In either case, you should work with your PGA/LPGA teaching professional to study your skills evaluation information and agree on which areas will be the focus of your improvement practice plan in the next step.

Practice With a Purpose

The final step on the road to improvement is to develop a plan to reach your goals. Once your highest priority improvement opportunities are identified, your PGA/LPGA professional can help you develop a productive practice plan that will focus on your skills improvement priorities.

As you develop your plan to practice with a purpose, consider how much time you spend practicing each area of your game as well as what you do when practicing those areas. Many times what is needed is not simply more hours of practice, but rather a different allocation of your practice time so that you are spending the right amount of time on the right areas of your game.

For example, most golfers love to hit drivers and full shots on the range. This is not a bad thing, as these are important shots in every round of golf. However, many people will spend 50% or more of their practice time hitting drivers and full shots, when in fact those shots account for only around 25% of strokes taken in an average round. On the other hand, short game shots around the green, including putting, account for nearly 60% of strokes taken. These critical scoring areas frequently receive only a small fraction of practice time.

The Don Law Golf Academy Skills Improvement Workbook will help you cover all of these areas of skills improvement. First, there are forms that you can use to collect information about your current skills level in all areas of your game. These worksheets include specific skills assessments as well as on-course performance statistics. Just through the act of doing these assessments and collecting the information you will learn many things about your own golf game and will be able to see your improvement in the numbers and your scores.

Once you identify areas that need improvement, this workbook also contains suggestions for practice drills and games that you can play – either alone or with a friend – to sharpen your skills. At the Don Law Golf Academy, we are strong proponents of using skill-based games to help make your practice time more enjoyable and purposeful. To that end, we have included a comprehensive suite of fun practice games (drills) that will help you focus on each specific skill measured in the evaluation process.

Background

The Don Law Golf Academy (DLGA), based in Boca Raton, Florida, was founded in 1999 by Don Law and his wife Diana, and is co-owned by their daughter Jennifer Moss and Rick Heard. DLGA provides a full suite of golf instruction programming to hundreds of junior and adult golfers. With three South Florida academy locations and 12 PGA/LPGA and apprentice teaching professionals, DLGA has one of the largest golf instruction programs in the United States.

DLGA staff have won numerous PGA awards for their teaching and PGA involvement. Don was named the national PGA Junior Leader in 2012, the highest honor for junior golf instruction. He was named South Florida PGA Section Golf Professional of the Year in 2011, and is a US Kids Master teaching professional. Rick was the Southeast Chapter PGA President for three terms ending in 2012, is a past Southeast Chapter Junior Leader, two-time PGA Horton Smith education award winner, and was named Chapter Golf Professional of the Year for 2010.

We believe it is critical to keep the golf learning process enjoyable. To that end, we incorporate fun practice games into our traditional instruction programs for players at all levels. In 2009, Don, Diana, and Rick teamed with PGA professionals Bill Scott and Chad Kurmel to form ParKit Golf, Inc.

Our teaching pros founded ParKit Golf to market our innovative practice games to other teaching professionals and serious students around the country. Many of our practice games are used in golf schools and by US Kids Golf certified instructors in classes and lessons for both juniors and adults. With this workbook, you can use those same tools to make your practice sessions more fun.

Through ParKit, the team created products comprised of more than two dozen fun, skill-based educational practice games developed and refined over the years teaching juniors and adults at

DLGA. ParKit's first product, the Professional Junior Training Kit, won a "Best New Product" award at the 2010 PGA Merchandise Show, and is used by PGA professionals around the country to add fun and excitement to junior classes and camps. ParKit's Short Game Training Kit is customized for serious students of any age who want to improve their short games and lower their scores.

This Skills Improvement Workbook is the marriage of these in-depth skills evaluation worksheets with ParKit's fun practice games. Traditionally, the skills evaluation process is conducted by an experienced PGA/LPGA professional who can then recommend a practice routine to focus on improvement.

The Workbook explains how you can complete the skills assessments on your own, and how to gather meaningful information on your golf game. Then, each skills area is linked to a suite of ParKit practice games that will help you focus on your improvement opportunities. It is not our intent that you go forward without professional assistance – only that you become empowered to better understand your own game. We strongly encourage you to seek the advice and assistance of an expert PGA/LPGA teacher who can provide instruction and coordinate your improvement plan.

It is our hope that this workbook will help you learn more about your golf game and guide you down the road to lower scores.

Rick Heard, PGA
Don Law, PGA

1

SKILLS EVALUATION WORKSHEETS

Before you can develop a plan to practice productively, you need to know which areas of your game need the most attention. This Skills Improvement Workbook contains skills assessment worksheets that you may use to collect skills data. These worksheets will provide you with the information necessary to understand your strengths and to identify your highest priority improvement opportunities.

The first line of each worksheet contains a "standard" line that shows benchmark skills results for a PGA professional golfer. You may use these as a guideline or a "standard of excellence" to work toward as you refine and improve your game.

You should make a habit of doing each evaluation at regular intervals – perhaps monthly or every two months. Record the date of each evaluation and monitor your progress over time.

The following pages contain detailed instructions for setting up each skills assessment and for using the worksheets.

Short Putt

Find a location on the putting green where you can putt from 3 feet to 15 feet from the hole with a slight break from left to right. Measure points at 3-foot intervals, beginning at 3 feet from the hole. Place a ball marker on each spot. When complete, you should have markers at 3', 6', 9', 12', and 15'. All putts should be along the same line, with a slight left to right break.

Begin at the 3' mark and attempt two putts. If you sink a putt, record a "0" on the worksheet. If the putt misses, record the distance in feet of each miss, always rounding up to the next number of feet. For example, any miss is "1." If you miss by 1½ feet, write down "2", and so on. Note whether your misses are due to distance control or aiming issues. Do this from each of the markers, then repeat from a different spot on the green with a slight left to right break.

Total your results from each side of the worksheet and compare to the standard. You should look for trends and differences in the results. Are you better with putts that break right or left? Is there a length of putt that is problematic? Is distance control a problem? Are you showing improvement from prior assessments? How do you compare to the PGA pro standard?

If you find an area that seems to need improvement, you should develop or modify your practice routine to focus more time on that area. Review the suggested practice games and incorporate one or more of them into your practice sessions.

Suggested practice games:
- Clockwork
- Line It Up
- School
- Sequence
- Wicket Trail

SKILLS IMPROVEMENT WORKBOOK

DLGA Skills Assessment Worksheet: Short Putt

Date	Breaking Left to Right										L-R TOTAL	Breaking Right to Left										R-L TOTAL	TOTAL ALL
	3'		6'		9'		12'		15'			3'		6'		9'		12'		15'			
	1	2	1	2	1	2	1	2	1	2		1	2	1	2	1	2	1	2	1	2		
Standard	0	0	0	0	1	0	1	1	1	2	6	0	0	0	0	0	1	1	0	2	1	5	11

20 putts in all. Take 2 putts from each distance. Record the resulting distance in feet from the hole for each putt. Record "0" if the ball finishes in the hole.

Long Putt

Find a place on the putting green where you can putt from 20 feet to 60 feet from the hole. Measure points at 20', 30', 40', 50', and 60' and place a ball marker on each spot. All putts should be along the same line.

Begin at the 20' mark and attempt two putts. If you sink a putt, record a "0" on the worksheet. If the putt misses, record the distance in feet of each miss, always rounding up to the next number of feet. For example, any miss is "1." If you miss by 1½ feet, write down "2", and so on. Do this from each of the markers, then total your results for all putts combined.

Total your results across each length of putt and compare to the standard. You should look for trends and differences in the results. Long putts require excellent distance control. Is there a length of putt that is problematic? Are you showing improvement from prior assessments? How do you compare to the PGA pro standard?

If you find an area that seems to need improvement, you should develop or modify your practice routine to focus more time on that area. Review the suggested practice games and incorporate one or more of them into your practice sessions.

Suggested practice games:
- Batter Up!
- Catch Me If You Can
- LagMaster
- Line It Up
- School
- Sequence
- Sneak Attack
- Wicket Trail

DLGA Skills Assessment Worksheet   Long Putt

Date	20'		30'		40'		50'		60'		TOTAL ALL
	1	2	1	2	1	2	1	2	1	2	
Standard	0	1	1	2	2	1	0	2	2	3	*14*

10 putts in all, to same hole from different distances. Take 2 putts from each distance. Record the resulting distance in feet from the hole for each putt. Record "0" if the ball finishes in the hole.

Chipping

Find a place on fringe of the putting green where you will have a good lie and can chip from 45 feet and 60 feet to different holes. All chips should be across a flat green with little or no break.

Begin at the 45' mark and attempt five chips. If you sink the chip, record a "0" on the worksheet. If the chip misses, record the distance in feet of each miss, always rounding up to the next number of feet. For example, any miss is "1." If you miss by 1½ feet, write down "2", and so on. If you miss by more than 20 feet, record "21." Do this from each distance and total your results for each distance.

Total your results from each side of the worksheet and compare to the standard. You should look for trends and differences in the results. Is there a length of chip that is problematic? Are you showing improvement from prior assessments? How do you compare to the PGA pro standard?

If you find an area that seems to need improvement, you should develop or modify your practice routine to focus more time on that area. Review the suggested practice games and incorporate one or more of them into your practice sessions.

Suggested practice games:
- Air Mail
- Batter Up!
- Catch Me If You Can
- Club Tricks
- Landing Zone
- Sequence
- Sneak Attack

DLGA Skills Assessment Worksheet: Chipping

Date	From 45 Feet					45' TOTAL	From 60 Feet					60' TOTAL	TOTAL ALL
	1	2	3	4	5		1	2	3	4	5		
Standard	1	0	1	3	2	7	1	2	1	3	2	9	16

10 shots in all, from the fringe. Take 5 shots from each distance. Measure and record the resulting distance in feet from the hole for each chip. Record "0" if the ball finishes in the hole. Record "21" if the ball finishes more than 20 feet from the hole.

Pitching

Find a place 15 yards from the edge of the putting green where you will have a good lie and can pitch approximately 25-30 yards from the hole. There should be around 10-15 yards from the edge of the green to the hole, in addition to the 15 yards from the pitching location to the edge of the green. Select a location where the ball can land and roll across a flat green with little or no break.

Attempt ten pitch shots. If you sink the shot, record a "0" on the worksheet. If the shot misses, record the distance in feet of each miss, always rounding up to the next number of feet. For example, any miss is "1." If you miss by 1½ feet, write down "2", and so on. If you miss by more than 20 feet, record "21." Total your results for all shots combined.

Total your results for all 10 shots and compare to the standard. You should look for trends and differences in the results. How consistent are you? Do your shots tend to come up short or go too long? Do you tend to hit pitch shots "thin" (not brushing the grass) or "fat" (hitting grass behind the ball)? Are you showing improvement from prior assessments? How do you compare to the PGA pro standard?

If you find an area that seems to need improvement, you should develop or modify your practice routine to focus more time on that area. Review the suggested practice games and incorporate one or more of them into your practice sessions.

Suggested practice games:
- Air Mail
- Batter Up!
- Catch Me (If You Can)
- Club Tricks
- Landing Zone
- Sequence
- Sneak Attack

DLGA Skills Assessment Worksheet: Pitching

Date	1	2	3	4	5	6	7	8	9	10	TOTAL
Standard	2	3	1	2	0	4	3	3	1	2	21

10 shots in all, from a good lie 20-25 yards from the green. Measure and record the resulting distance in feet from the hole for each shot. Record "0" if the ball finishes in the hole. Record "21" if the ball finishes more than 20 feet from the hole.

Bunkers

Find a place in a greenside bunker where you will have a good lie about 10-15 yards from the hole. The shot should be across a flat green with little or no break.

Attempt ten bunker shots. Rake the bunker as necessary between shots so that each shot is from a nice flat lie If you sink the shot, record a "0" on the worksheet. If the shot misses, record the distance in feet of each miss, always rounding up to the next number of feet. For example, any miss is "1." If you miss by 1½ feet, write down "2", and so on. If you miss by more than 20 feet, record "21." Total your results for all shots combined.

Total your results for all 10 shots and compare to the standard. You should look for trends and differences in the results. How consistent are you? Do your shots tend to come up short or go too long? Do you tend to hit bunker shots "thin" (not taking enough sand) or "fat" (hitting too much sand or too far behind the ball)? Are you showing improvement from prior assessments? How do you compare to the PGA pro standard?

If you find an area that seems to need improvement, you should develop or modify your practice routine to focus more time on that area. Review the suggested practice games and incorporate one or more of them into your practice sessions.

Suggested practice games:
- Air Mail
- Batter Up!
- Catch Me If You Can
- Club Tricks
- Landing Zone
- Sequence
- Sneak Attack

DLGA Skills Assessment Worksheet: Bunkers

Date	1	2	3	4	5	6	7	8	9	10	TOTAL
Standard	5	2	4	4	6	2	1	3	2	4	33

10 shots in all, from a good lie in a greenside bunker. Measure and record the resulting distance in feet from the hole for each shot. Record "0" if the ball finishes in the hole. Record "21" if the ball finishes more than 20 feet from the hole.

Approach Shots

Find a place in a fairway where you can hit approach shots to a green. If this is not possible, you may use the driving range if you will be able to measure how far away your shots will come to rest from a target. Use a laser range finder and measure points at 20, 40, 60, 80, and 100 yards from the hole or your range target. It is best to do this assessment with a partner who can measure and record each shot after you hit it.

Begin at the 20 yard mark and attempt two shots. Record the distance in feet that each ball comes to rest from the hole or target, always rounding up to the next number of feet. For example, if the ball finishes 1½ feet from the hole, write down "2", and so on. If your ball finishes more than 40 feet from the hole, record "41." Do the same from each yardage.

Total your results for all 10 shots and compare to the standard. You should look for trends and differences in the results. How consistent are you? Is there a distance that is more difficult for you? Are you changing clubs as the distances change, or do you use the same club for each shot? Do your shots tend to come up short or go too long? Is there a pattern of missing to the right or to the left? Are you showing improvement from prior assessments? How do you compare to the PGA pro standard?

If you find an area that seems to need improvement, you should develop or modify your practice routine to focus more time on that area. Review the suggested practice games and incorporate one or more of them into your practice sessions.

Suggested practice games:
- Air Mail
- Catch Me If You Can
- Club Tricks
- Sequence
- Sneak Attack

DLGA Skills Assessment Worksheet: Approach Shots

Date	20 Yards		40 Yards		60 Yards		80 Yards		100 Yards		TOTAL ALL
	1	2	1	2	1	2	1	2	1	2	
Standard	2	3	5	11	11	12	9	15	12	10	90

10 shots in all. Take 2 shots from each distance. Record the resulting distance in feet from the hole for each shot. Record "0" if the shot finishes in the hole. Record "41" if the ball finishes more than 40 feet from the hole.

Carry Distances

Every golfer needs to know the exact yardage the ball carries with each club. This worksheet provides a way for you to record your carry distances with your pitching wedge, 6-iron and 3-wood. Your distances with other clubs probably increase in 7-10 yard increments, but you can also measure them individually and record them on another worksheet.

Using each club from a good lie in the fairway or on the driving range, hit five balls. Watch where each shot lands and measure the distance with a laser range finder. It is best to do this assessment with a partner who can measure and record each shot after you hit it. Record the yardage on the worksheet.

Pay close attention to your results, especially to variations in carry distance. You want to be able to hit each club with consistent, predictable carry yardages to help you make the proper club selection on the course. If you have wide variations due to poor shots, exclude those from the averages and use only the more consistent shots. Then, think about those poor shots and their causes. Use face impact tape to determine whether you are consistently hitting the ball on the "sweet spot." Do you tend to hit these shots "thin" (not brushing the grass) or "fat" (hitting the grass behind the ball)?

If you find an area that seems to need improvement, you should develop or modify your practice routine to focus more time on that area. Review the suggested practice games and incorporate one or more of them into your practice sessions.

Suggested practice games:
- Air Mail
- Catch Me If You Can
- Sequence
- Sneak Attack

DLGA Skills Assessment Worksheet: Carry Distances

Date	Standard														
	Wedge					**6-Iron**					**3-Wood**				
	1	2	3	4	5	1	2	3	4	5	1	2	3	4	5
Standard	121	125	126	123	123	162	165	155	159	161	230	236	225	231	228

15 shots in all. Hit 5 shots with a full swing with each club. Measure and record the actual total distance the ball travels in the air (use a laser measuring device, or place cones or other markers on the range at known distances).

Nine Ball Flights

This worksheet helps you measure your ability to control your golf ball. Golf seldom demands perfectly straight shots, and you need to be able to work the ball, making it curve and controlling its trajectory at will. This skill is especially important in poor weather conditions and for trouble shots, where you might need to hit shots low or high, or curve the ball around obstacles.

Do this assessment at the range, and work through the nine ball flights. Try to make the ball hook, go straight, and slice on command. Try to hit low, medium, and high shots. Record a "1" on the worksheet if you are successful at a particular shot, and total your score to see if you can score 9 points.

You should incorporate the Nine Ball Flights into every practice session... it is fun to practice controlling your ball flight. And, learning to hook and slice the ball at will can be the best way to learn to hit the ball straight.

DLGA Skills Assessment Worksheet: Nine Ball Flights

Date	Low Hook	Medium Hook	High Hook	Low Straight	Medium Straight	High Straight	Low Slice	Medium Slice	High Slice	TOTAL
Standard	1	1	1	1	1	1	1	1	1	9

The purpose is to learn to control the ball flight. Make 1 attempt at each shot, trying to hit the type of shot described in each column. Record a "1" if you succeed in hitting the shot.

2

ON-COURSE PERFORMANCE

The second and perhaps best way to evaluate your skill level is through your performance during actual rounds of golf where you play by USGA rules. If you are already playing tournament golf, these are perfect opportunities to learn more about your performance. If not, you can still play rounds and record your statistics.

The following "stats scorecard" provides a way to record some of your most important performance statistics as you play. Bring this scorecard with you and enter your results at the end of each hole, as you would normally write down your score. A sample filled-in scorecard is shown from an actual tournament round.

A common mistake in collecting performance data is to try to capture too much information. Sometimes, all that is really needed is stats on greens hit in regulation scrambling, and putting. However, if you really want to understand the factors that are driving your scores, you should record all of your results from this scorecard.

In order to capture the information quickly, it is important to keep the process simple. If you use the following method, you will be able to maintain useful performance statistics on each round of golf. Here are suggestions for each entry line:

Performance Statistics Scorecard Instructions

Par – Enter the hole-by-hole par for the course you are playing.

Hit Fairway – Enter a code for the club used from the tee on par 4 and par 5 holes (e.g. "D" for driver). Circle or otherwise mark the box if the shot finds the fairway.

Green in Regulation – Enter the club used for the approach to the green. Circle or otherwise mark the box if the shot finds the green.

Scramble Attempt – Enter the club used for a chip or pitch from around the green. Circle or otherwise mark the box if you successfully scramble (get on the green and 1-putt).

Greenside Bunker – Enter the club used for a bunker shot. Circle or otherwise mark the box if you get on the green and 1-putt.

Penalties – Enter a code as shown on the card for any penalties you may incur, such as out of bounds, water hazard, lost ball, etc.

Putts – Enter the number of putts, counting only shots taken from the green. If the ball is off the green it is a scramble attempt.

Score – Record your score for the hole.

When you are finished recording your information for a round, take time to look over your stats and understand what you did well and what areas need improvement.

SAMPLE COMPLETED SCORECARD

DLGA Performance Statistics Scorecard   Date: 11/4/12   Course: Your Country Club

Hole	1	2	3	4	5	6	7	8	9	TOTAL
Par	5	4	3	5	4	3	4	3	5	36
Hit Fairway	D	D		D	D		D		D	5
Green in Regulation	3W	GW	4	8	PW	5	6	4	5	7
Scramble Attempt		P	P						SW	3
Greenside Bunker										
Penalties										
# Putts	2	1	1	1	2	2	2	2	2	15
Score	4	4	3	4	4	3	4	3	5	34

Green in Regulation means on the green in 1 shot on par 3, 2 shots on par 4, and 3 shots on par 5 holes.
Scramble Attempt means shots taken (with any club) within 15 yards of the green.

Penalties coded as follows:

OB	out of bounds	W	water hazard
U	unplayable lie	L	lost ball
B	ball moved	O	other

DLGA Performance Statistics Scorecard	Date:					Course:				
Hole	1	2	3	4	5	6	7	8	9	TOTAL
Par										
Hit Fairway										
Green in Regulation										
Scramble Attempt										
Greenside Bunker										
Penalties										
# Putts										
Score										

Green in Regulation means on the green in 1 shot on par 3, 2 shots on par 4, and 3 shots on par 5 holes.
Scramble Attempt means shots taken (with any club) within 15 yards of the green.

Penalties coded as follows:	OB	out of bounds	W	water hazard
	U	unplayable lie	L	lost ball
	B	ball moved	O	other

DLGA Performance Statistics Scorecard Date:							Course:			
Hole	1	2	3	4	5	6	7	8	9	TOTAL
Par										
Hit Fairway										
Green in Regulation										
Scramble Attempt										
Greenside Bunker										
Penalties										
# Putts										
Score										

Green in Regulation means on the green in 1 shot on par 3, 2 shots on par 4, and 3 shots on par 5 holes. Scramble Attempt means shots taken (with any club) within 15 yards of the green.

Penalties coded as follows:

OB	out of bounds	W	water hazard
U	unplayable lie	L	lost ball
B	ball moved	O	other

DLGA Performance Statistics Scorecard	Date:								Course:		
Hole	1	2	3	4	5	6	7	8	9	TOTAL
Par										
Hit Fairway										
Green in Regulation										
Scramble Attempt										
Greenside Bunker										
Penalties										
# Putts										
Score										

Green in Regulation means on the green in 1 shot on par 3, 2 shots on par 4, and 3 shots on par 5 holes.
Scramble Attempt means shots taken (with any club) within 15 yards of the green.

Penalties coded as follows:	OB out of bounds	W water hazard
	U unplayable lie	L lost ball
	B ball moved	O other

DLGA Performance Statistics Scorecard	Date:						Course:			
Hole	1	2	3	4	5	6	7	8	9	TOTAL
Par										
Hit Fairway										
Green in Regulation										
Scramble Attempt										
Greenside Bunker										
Penalties										
# Putts										
Score										

Green in Regulation means on the green in 1 shot on par 3, 2 shots on par 4, and 3 shots on par 5 holes.
Scramble Attempt means shots taken (with any club) within 15 yards of the green.

Penalties coded as follows:

OB	out of bounds	W	water hazard
U	unplayable lie	L	lost ball
B	ball moved	O	other

DLGA Performance Statistics Scorecard   Date: Course:

Hole	1	2	3	4	5	6	7	8	9	TOTAL
Par										
Hit Fairway										
Green in Regulation										
Scramble Attempt										
Greenside Bunker										
Penalties										
# Putts										
Score										

Green in Regulation means on the green in 1 shot on par 3, 2 shots on par 4, and 3 shots on par 5 holes.
Scramble Attempt means shots taken (with any club) within 15 yards of the green.

Penalties coded as follows:		
OB out of bounds	W water hazard	
U unplayable lie	L lost ball	
B ball moved	O other	

DLGA Performance Statistics Scorecard   Date: Course:

Hole	1	2	3	4	5	6	7	8	9	TOTAL
Par										
Hit Fairway										
Green in Regulation										
Scramble Attempt										
Greenside Bunker										
Penalties										
# Putts										
Score										

Green in Regulation means on the green in 1 shot on par 3, 2 shots on par 4, and 3 shots on par 5 holes. Scramble Attempt means shots taken (with any club) within 15 yards of the green.

Penalties coded as follows:

OB	out of bounds	W water hazard
U	unplayable lie	L lost ball
B	ball moved	O other

DLGA Performance Statistics Scorecard Date:										Course:
Hole	1	2	3	4	5	6	7	8	9	TOTAL
Par										
Hit Fairway										
Green in Regulation										
Scramble Attempt										
Greenside Bunker										
Penalties										
# Putts										
Score										

Green in Regulation means on the green in 1 shot on par 3, 2 shots on par 4, and 3 shots on par 5 holes. Scramble Attempt means shots taken (with any club) within 15 yards of the green.

Penalties coded as follows:	OB out of bounds	W water hazard
	U unplayable lie	L lost ball
	B ball moved	O other

DLGA Performance Statistics Scorecard	Date:						Course:			
Hole	1	2	3	4	5	6	7	8	9	TOTAL
Par										
Hit Fairway										
Green in Regulation										
Scramble Attempt										
Greenside Bunker										
Penalties										
# Putts										
Score										

Green in Regulation means on the green in 1 shot on par 3, 2 shots on par 4, and 3 shots on par 5 holes.
Scramble Attempt means shots taken (with any club) within 15 yards of the green.

Penalties coded as follows:	OB out of bounds	W water hazard
	U unplayable lie	L lost ball
	B ball moved	O other

DLGA Performance Statistics Scorecard Date: Course:

Hole	1	2	3	4	5	6	7	8	9	TOTAL
Par										
Hit Fairway										
Green in Regulation										
Scramble Attempt										
Greenside Bunker										
Penalties										
# Putts										
Score										

Green in Regulation means on the green in 1 shot on par 3, 2 shots on par 4, and 3 shots on par 5 holes. Scramble Attempt means shots taken (with any club) within 15 yards of the green.

Penalties coded as follows:	OB	out of bounds	W	water hazard
	U	unplayable lie	L	lost ball
	B	ball moved	O	other

DLGA Performance Statistics Scorecard Date:								Course:		
Hole	1	2	3	4	5	6	7	8	9	TOTAL
Par										
Hit Fairway										
Green in Regulation										
Scramble Attempt										
Greenside Bunker										
Penalties										
# Putts										
Score										

Green in Regulation means on the green in 1 shot on par 3, 2 shots on par 4, and 3 shots on par 5 holes.
Scramble Attempt means shots taken (with any club) within 15 yards of the green.

Penalties coded as follows:			
OB	out of bounds	W	water hazard
U	unplayable lie	L	lost ball
B	ball moved	O	other

3

PRODUCTIVE AND FUN PRACTICE GAMES

If you want to improve your golf game, there are no shortcuts. You must practice, and you must practice the right areas. It sounds difficult, and it is, but practice does not have to be boring! Through our extensive work teaching both juniors and adults, we have developed many fun, skill-based games that convert boring practice drills into fun activities.

Once you complete the above skills evaluations and know what areas of your game you need to focus on, these games will help you sharpen your skills. Each skills area in chapter 2 lists the games that apply to that skill. Choose one or more games from the list and you will be ready to get started lowering your scores.

In this chapter you will find complete instructions for playing all 12 practice games. Many of the games use aiming rings that help focus on a target. These tools can be found at ParKit Golf's website www.parkitgolf.com, along with a complete short game practice kit for seriously fun practice. Have fun practicing!

AIR MAIL

Air Mail is a more challenging version of "Catch Me (If You Can)." Air Mail helps develop chipping and pitching technique and distance control, and can also be used for full shots. The object is to make each ball fly farther in the air than the prior ball without going past a maximum distance boundary.

Equipment Required:

✓ Supply of golf balls (either regular balls or range balls)
✓ 2 ball markers or tees

Setup: Please refer to the drawing on the facing page.

➤ Create a starting point by placing 2 ball markers or tees 6 feet apart in an area suitable for chipping, pitching or bunker shots.

➤ Create an out-of-bounds limit so that the game will end when a ball travels beyond the limit. This could be the edge of the green, a string stretched across the green, or some other area. This limit should be about 35 yards away from the starting point.

How To Play:

➤ The goal is to hit (either a chip, pitch, or bunker shot) as many balls in a row as possible where each ball flies farther in the air than the prior ball ("target ball") without going beyond the "out-of-bounds" limit. Each ball must "air mail" the target ball.

➤ Each player begins by hitting a ball a short distance, scoring 1 point. That ball becomes the target ball for the next shot. The player then hits a second ball. If that ball flies over the target

AIR MAIL

ball and stops before going out-of-bounds, score another point and that ball becomes the new target ball.

➤ If the ball lands on top of the target ball, the shot scores a point and the new target ball is whichever ball comes to rest farther from the player.

➤ Continue hitting until a ball either fails to air mail the target ball or the ball goes too far (out-of-bounds). Score a point each time the ball air mails the target ball and stays in bounds.

➤ If playing individually, keep a record of the number of points you score, and attempt to set a new record each time you play the game.

➤ If competing with multiple players, the winner is the player with the most points, once all players have had an equal number of turns.

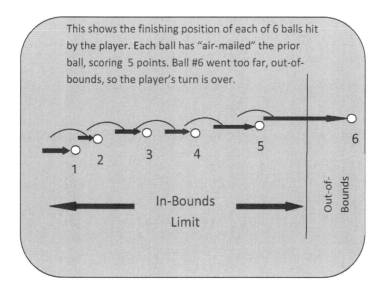

This shows the finishing position of each of 6 balls hit by the player. Each ball has "air-mailed" the prior ball, scoring 5 points. Ball #6 went too far, out-of-bounds, so the player's turn is over.

In-Bounds Limit

Out-of-Bounds

AIR MAIL

Date	Subject (circle one)	Boundary Limit Distance	Number of Points
	Chip-Pitch-Bunker-Full		
	Chip-Pitch-Bunker-Full		
	Chip-Pitch-Bunker-Full		
	Chip-Pitch-Bunker-Full		
	Chip-Pitch-Bunker-Full		
	Chip-Pitch-Bunker-Full		
	Chip-Pitch-Bunker-Full		
	Chip-Pitch-Bunker-Full		
	Chip-Pitch-Bunker-Full		
	Chip-Pitch-Bunker-Full		
	Chip-Pitch-Bunker-Full		
	Chip-Pitch-Bunker-Full		
	Chip-Pitch-Bunker-Full		
	Chip-Pitch-Bunker-Full		

AIR MAIL

Date	Subject (circle one)	Boundary Limit Distance	Number of Points
	Chip-Pitch-Bunker-Full		
	Chip-Pitch-Bunker-Full		
	Chip-Pitch-Bunker-Full		
	Chip-Pitch-Bunker-Full		
	Chip-Pitch-Bunker-Full		
	Chip-Pitch-Bunker-Full		
	Chip-Pitch-Bunker-Full		
	Chip-Pitch-Bunker-Full		
	Chip-Pitch-Bunker-Full		
	Chip-Pitch-Bunker-Full		
	Chip-Pitch-Bunker-Full		
	Chip-Pitch-Bunker-Full		
	Chip-Pitch-Bunker-Full		
	Chip-Pitch-Bunker-Full		

BATTER UP!

Batter Up! can be used for all short game situations, and is excellent for practicing both distance and directional control. The object is to be able to repeat your swing and be able to hit each ball to the same spot on the green. You can hit it there once… can you do it again and again?

<u>Equipment Required</u>:

- ✓ 3' and 6' ParZone rings
- ✓ 10 golf balls, including 1 colored ball

<u>Setup</u>: Please refer to the drawing on the facing page.

➢ Select a flat area of the putting green away from any hole.

➢ Place the 10 balls together either on the green (if putting) or off the green (if chipping, pitching, or hitting bunker shots).

➢ Set the ParZone rings aside until all 10 balls have been hit.

<u>How To Play</u>:

➢ The object of the game is to achieve the highest possible "batting average" by consistently hitting the 10 balls to the same spot.

➢ Begin by hitting the colored ball toward an open area on the green (not toward a hole).

➢ Pay close attention to where this colored ball comes to rest. Then, continue hitting the nine remaining balls, trying to make each ball come to rest in the exact same place as the colored ball.

BATTER UP!

➢ After you have hit all 10 balls, select either the 3' or 6' Par-Zone ring and place it over the largest cluster of balls that includes the colored ball.

➢ Count the number of balls that are within the ring and multiply this number by 100; that is your "batting average."

➢ Keep a record of your batting average, and attempt to set a new record each time you play the game.

➢ If competing with multiple players, the winner is the player with the highest batting average.

➢ If the ParZone rings is too small to frequently encircle more than one ball, use the larger ring until your skill level improves.

➢ Try this game blindfolded! After hitting the first ball, close your eyes or wear a blindfold and see how well you do.

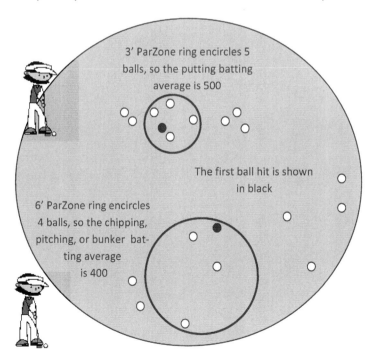

BATTER UP!

Date	Subject (circle one)	Ring Size (circle one)	Number of Balls In Ring
	Putt Chip Pitch Bunker	3' 6'	
	Putt Chip Pitch Bunker	3' 6'	
	Putt Chip Pitch Bunker	3' 6'	
	Putt Chip Pitch Bunker	3' 6'	
	Putt Chip Pitch Bunker	3' 6'	
	Putt Chip Pitch Bunker	3' 6'	
	Putt Chip Pitch Bunker	3' 6'	
	Putt Chip Pitch Bunker	3' 6'	
	Putt Chip Pitch Bunker	3' 6'	
	Putt Chip Pitch Bunker	3' 6'	
	Putt Chip Pitch Bunker	3' 6'	
	Putt Chip Pitch Bunker	3' 6'	

BATTER UP!

Date	Subject (circle one)	Ring Size (circle one)	Number of Balls In Ring
	Putt Chip Pitch Bunker	3' 6'	
	Putt Chip Pitch Bunker	3' 6'	
	Putt Chip Pitch Bunker	3' 6'	
	Putt Chip Pitch Bunker	3' 6'	
	Putt Chip Pitch Bunker	3' 6'	
	Putt Chip Pitch Bunker	3' 6'	
	Putt Chip Pitch Bunker	3' 6'	
	Putt Chip Pitch Bunker	3' 6'	
	Putt Chip Pitch Bunker	3' 6'	
	Putt Chip Pitch Bunker	3' 6'	
	Putt Chip Pitch Bunker	3' 6'	
	Putt Chip Pitch Bunker	3' 6'	
	Putt Chip Pitch Bunker	3' 6'	

CATCH ME (IF YOU CAN)

Catch Me (If You Can) helps develop distance control for all types of shots, including putting, chipping, pitching, bunkers, and even full shots. The object is simple: hit each ball farther than the prior ball – as many times as possible.

Equipment Required:

- ✓ Supply of golf balls (either regular balls or range balls)
- ✓ 2 ball markers or tees

Setup: Please refer to the drawing on the facing page.

➤ Create a starting point by placing 2 ball markers or tees 6 feet apart either on the green (for putting) or in an area suitable for chipping, pitching, bunkers or full shots.

➤ Create an out-of-bounds limit so that the game will end when a ball travels beyond the limit. For putting, this could be the edge of the green, a string stretched across the green, or some other area. For chipping, pitching, and bunkers, this could be a line about 25 yards away from the starting point. For full shots it could be a yardage marker.

How To Play:

➤ The goal is to hit as many balls in a row as possible where each ball travels farther than the prior ball ("target ball") without going beyond the "out-of-bounds" limit. Each ball must "catch up to" the target ball.

➤ Each player begins by hitting a ball a short distance, scoring 1 point. That ball becomes the target ball for the next shot. The player then hits a second ball. If that ball catches or passes the

CATCH ME (IF YOU CAN)

target ball, score another point and that ball becomes the new target ball for the next shot.

➢ If the ball strikes the target ball, the shot scores a point and the new target ball is whichever ball comes to rest farther from the player.

➢ Continue hitting until a ball either fails to catch the target ball or the ball goes too far (out-of-bounds). Score a point each time the ball catches or passes the target ball.

➢ If playing individually, keep a record of the number of points you score, and attempt to set a new record each time you play the game.

➢ If competing with multiple players, the winner is the player with the most points, once all players have had an equal number of turns.

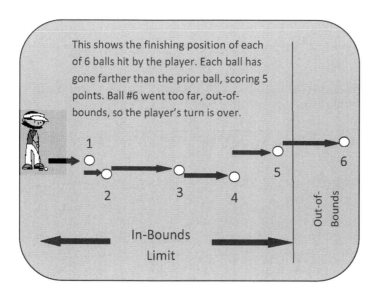

This shows the finishing position of each of 6 balls hit by the player. Each ball has gone farther than the prior ball, scoring 5 points. Ball #6 went too far, out-of-bounds, so the player's turn is over.

CATCH ME (IF YOU CAN)

Date	Subject (circle one)	Boundary Limit Distance	Number of Points
	Putt-Chip-Pitch-Bunker-Full		
	Putt-Chip-Pitch-Bunker-Full		
	Putt-Chip-Pitch-Bunker-Full		
	Putt-Chip-Pitch-Bunker-Full		
	Putt-Chip-Pitch-Bunker-Full		
	Putt-Chip-Pitch-Bunker-Full		
	Putt-Chip-Pitch-Bunker-Full		
	Putt-Chip-Pitch-Bunker-Full		
	Putt-Chip-Pitch-Bunker-Full		
	Putt-Chip-Pitch-Bunker-Full		
	Putt-Chip-Pitch-Bunker-Full		
	Putt-Chip-Pitch-Bunker-Full		
	Putt-Chip-Pitch-Bunker-Full		
	Putt-Chip-Pitch-Bunker-Full		

CATCH ME (IF YOU CAN)

Date	Subject (circle one)	Boundary Limit Distance	Number of Points
	Putt-Chip-Pitch-Bunker-Full		
	Putt-Chip-Pitch-Bunker-Full		
	Putt-Chip-Pitch-Bunker-Full		
	Putt-Chip-Pitch-Bunker-Full		
	Putt-Chip-Pitch-Bunker-Full		
	Putt-Chip-Pitch-Bunker-Full		
	Putt-Chip-Pitch-Bunker-Full		
	Putt-Chip-Pitch-Bunker-Full		
	Putt-Chip-Pitch-Bunker-Full		
	Putt-Chip-Pitch-Bunker-Full		
	Putt-Chip-Pitch-Bunker-Full		
	Putt-Chip-Pitch-Bunker-Full		
	Putt-Chip-Pitch-Bunker-Full		
	Putt-Chip-Pitch-Bunker-Full		

CLOCKWORK

Clockwork is a circle putting drill that focuses on short putts (usually 2nd putts) from all angles around the hole. The object is to sink as many putts in a row as possible, working your way around the hole like the hands of a clock.

Equipment Required:

- ✓ Up to 12 golf balls
- ✓ 3' and 6' ParZone target rings

Setup: Please refer to the drawing on the facing page.

➤ For short putts, place the 6' ParZone ring around a hole on the putting green and place 6 golf balls in a circle around the hole, using the ring as a guide in placing the balls. Space the balls evenly as shown in the diagram. Remove the ring when all balls are in place.

➤ For long putts, use the 3' ParZone ring as a target instead of the hole, and place up to 12 golf balls in a circle the desired distance from the ParZone target ring (e.g. 20').

How To Play:

➤ Beginning with any ball, putt toward the hole (or ParZone ring, depending on the above setup).

➤ If the ball is holed or (for long putts) finishes in the ParZone target ring, continue putting the next ball. If the ball is not holed or does not finish within the ParZone target ring, the player's turn ends and the balls are reset for the next player or

CLOCKWORK

next round. Continue putting, adding more balls as necessary, until a putt misses the hole (or ParZone ring).

➤ Score one point for each ball that is either holed or finishes inside the ParZone target rings.

➤ If playing individually, keep a record of the number of points you score, and attempt to set a new record each time you play the game.

➤ If competing with multiple players, the winner is the player with the most points, once all players have had an equal number of turns.

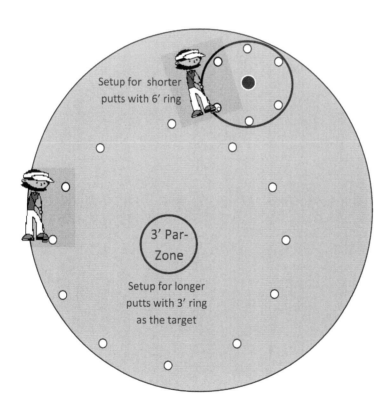

Setup for shorter putts with 6' ring

3' Par-Zone

Setup for longer putts with 3' ring as the target

CLOCKWORK

Date	Target (circle one)	Number of Putts In A Row
	Hole 3'Ring	
	Hole 3'Ring	
	Hole 3'Ring	
	Hole 3'Ring	
	Hole 3'Ring	
	Hole 3'Ring	
	Hole 3'Ring	
	Hole 3'Ring	
	Hole 3'Ring	
	Hole 3'Ring	
	Hole 3'Ring	
	Hole 3'Ring	
	Hole 3'Ring	
	Hole 3'Ring	

CLOCKWORK

Date	Target (circle one)		Number of Putts In A Row
	Hole	3'Ring	
	Hole	3'Ring	
	Hole	3'Ring	
	Hole	3'Ring	
	Hole	3'Ring	
	Hole	3'Ring	
	Hole	3'Ring	
	Hole	3'Ring	
	Hole	3'Ring	
	Hole	3'Ring	
	Hole	3'Ring	
	Hole	3'Ring	
	Hole	3'Ring	
	Hole	3'Ring	

CLUB TRICKS

Club Tricks helps you learn that you can successfully hit a shot with many different clubs. The object is to learn to use a variety of clubs for a particular shot, and ultimately to be able to select the best club for each situation. For any given shot, you may have a choice of several clubs. You should always try to choose the easiest and most reliable club for each shot.

Equipment Required:

- ✓ 6' ParZone ring
- ✓ 12 colored golf balls – 4 each in 3 colors
- ✓ Selection of golf clubs (e.g., sand wedge, wedge, and 8-iron)

Setup: Please refer to the drawing on the facing page.

➢ Select an area of the putting green away from any hole and place the 6' ParZone ring on the green.

➢ Place the 12 balls off the green in 3 color-coded groups, each with 4 balls.

How To Play:

➢ The object of the game is to hit all 12 balls into the ParZone target ring, using three different clubs for the same shot. In doing so, you will learn how to control your ball with different clubs. You will also learn which clubs are best for certain types of shots.

➢ Begin by selecting a club and hitting the first four colored balls toward the ParZone target ring. Pay attention to how easy or difficult it is to hit the balls into the ParZone ring. Your goal is to learn which club is the easiest to use for the situation.

CLUB TRICKS

➤ After hitting the first four balls, select a different club and repeat the above with the next four colored balls. Using the third club, repeat again with the remaining colored balls.

➤ Compare the number of balls that were within the target ring for each club. Pay attention to which group of balls are the least consistent or farthest from the target ring.

➤ Replace the club that produced the worst results with a different club and repeat the entire game from the same situation.

➤ Through the process of elimination, discover the club that is the easiest to use for the situation.

➤ Keep a record of which clubs are the easiest to use in different situations.

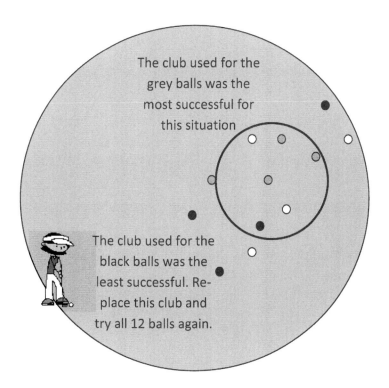

CLUB TRICKS

Date	Describe the Situation	Best Club for Situation

CLUB TRICKS

Date	Describe the Situation	Best Club for Situation

LAGMASTER

LagMaster is a putting distance control game that focuses on both long and short putts. The object is to hole each ball in the fewest strokes possible.

Equipment Required:

- ✓ 5 balls
- ✓ 4 ball markers or tees
- ✓ 6' ParZone ring

Setup: Please refer to the drawing on the facing page.

➤ Place the 6' ParZone ring around a hole on the putting green as shown.

➤ Place the ball markers 5 feet, 10 feet, 20 feet, and 40 feet from the hole.

How To Play:

➤ Beginning with all 5 balls at the 40' marker, putt each ball toward the hole surrounded by the ParZone target ring, counting each stroke.

➤ Any ball that is holed is removed from future play.

➤ Any ball that finishes within the ParZone target ring is moved to the next closest marker.

➤ Continue putting the remaining balls from the same marker until each ball is either holed or finishes within the ParZone target ring. Remember to count each stroke.

LAGMASTER

➢ When all remaining balls have reached the closest marker (the 5' marker), remove the ParZone ring and putt the remaining balls to the hole until all of the balls are holed, continuing to count each stroke.

➢ The game is over when all 5 balls have been holed from any distance.

➢ Keep a record of the number of putts you require to hole all five balls and attempt to set a new (lower) record each time you play.

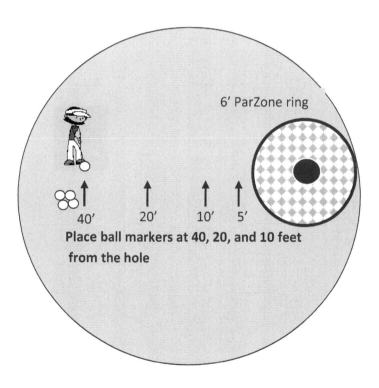

LAGMASTER

Date	Size of ParZone ring Used (circle one)		Number of Putts Required to Hole 5 Balls
	3'	6'	
	3'	6'	
	3'	6'	
	3'	6'	
	3'	6'	
	3'	6'	
	3'	6'	
	3'	6'	
	3'	6'	
	3'	6'	
	3'	6'	
	3'	6'	
	3'	6'	
	3'	6'	

LAGMASTER

Date	Size of ParZone ring Used (circle one)		Number of Putts Required to Hole 5 Balls
	3'	6'	
	3'	6'	
	3'	6'	
	3'	6'	
	3'	6'	
	3'	6'	
	3'	6'	
	3'	6'	
	3'	6'	
	3'	6'	
	3'	6'	
	3'	6'	
	3'	6'	
	3'	6'	

LANDING ZONE

Landing Zone helps develop distance and directional control for short game shots. When hitting shots from around the green, focus on where the ball should land in order to roll to the hole. The object is to land the ball in the correct spot for chipping, pitching, and bunker shots.

Equipment Required:

- ✓ 3' and 6' ParZone rings
- ✓ 2 ball markers

Setup: Please refer to the drawing on the facing page.

➢ Place 2 ball markers or tees 6 feet apart in an area suitable for chipping, pitching or bunker shots of any length. Many setups are possible, depending on whether you are playing the game while chipping, pitching, or hitting bunker shots. Place a supply of golf balls in the station.

➢ Place the 3' or 6' ParZone ring on the green or another suitable landing place. Try to determine where the ball should land in order to roll to your target (the hole or other target).

How To Play:

➢ The object of the game is to land your ball inside the ParZone target ring as many times in a row as possible.

➢ Keep a record of the number of times in a row you are able to land a ball inside the ParZone target ring, and attempt to set a new record each time you play the game.

LANDING ZONE

➤ Practice using different clubs while chipping or pitching, continuing to land the ball within the ParZone target ring. Pay close attention to where the ball ends up with different clubs.

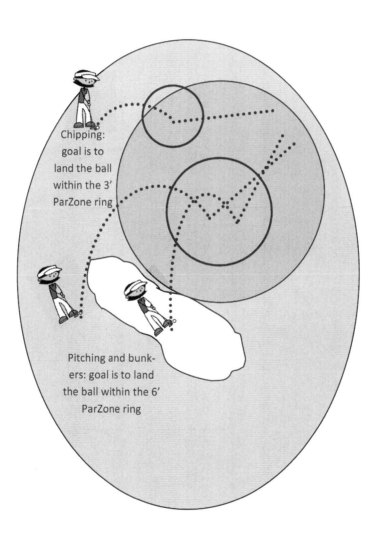

Chipping: goal is to land the ball within the 3' ParZone ring

Pitching and bunkers: goal is to land the ball within the 6' ParZone ring

LANDING ZONE

Date	Subject (circle one)	Ring Size (circle one)		Number of Balls In Ring
	Chip Pitch Bunker	3'	6'	
	Chip Pitch Bunker	3'	6'	
	Chip Pitch Bunker	3'	6'	
	Chip Pitch Bunker	3'	6'	
	Chip Pitch Bunker	3'	6'	
	Chip Pitch Bunker	3'	6'	
	Chip Pitch Bunker	3'	6'	
	Chip Pitch Bunker	3'	6'	
	Chip Pitch Bunker	3'	6'	
	Chip Pitch Bunker	3'	6'	
	Chip Pitch Bunker	3'	6'	
	Chip Pitch Bunker	3'	6'	
	Chip Pitch Bunker	3'	6'	
	Chip Pitch Bunker	3'	6'	

LANDING ZONE

Date	Subject (circle one)	Ring Size (circle one)		Number of Balls In Ring
	Chip Pitch Bunker	3'	6'	
	Chip Pitch Bunker	3'	6'	
	Chip Pitch Bunker	3'	6'	
	Chip Pitch Bunker	3'	6'	
	Chip Pitch Bunker	3'	6'	
	Chip Pitch Bunker	3'	6'	
	Chip Pitch Bunker	3'	6'	
	Chip Pitch Bunker	3'	6'	
	Chip Pitch Bunker	3'	6'	
	Chip Pitch Bunker	3'	6'	
	Chip Pitch Bunker	3'	6'	
	Chip Pitch Bunker	3'	6'	
	Chip Pitch Bunker	3'	6'	
	Chip Pitch Bunker	3'	6'	

LINE IT UP

Line It Up helps focus on putting directional control by helping you learn to roll the ball in a perfectly straight line. Line It Up is also friendly for greenskeepers who do not like chalk putting lines on the green.

<u>Equipment Required</u>:

- ✓ 5 golf balls
- ✓ ParKit Golf putting pins and string

<u>Setup</u>: Please refer to the drawing on the facing page.

➢ Find a flat portion of the putting green where you will have a straight putt. You can find a straight putt on a sloped green by making a few test rolls to the hole from different locations.

➢ Tie a 10 foot length of string to the pins and push one putting pin into the green about 3" behind the hole.

➢ Push the other putting pin into the green about 10' from the hole at the spot from which you will have a straight putt and tighten so that the string is taut. The string should be a few inches off the green.

<u>How To Play</u>:

➢ Place a ball directly under the string. Paying attention to the path of your club head compared to the string, putt the ball toward the hole. The ball should stay on line with the string. Continue putting until you miss, scoring a point for each holed putt.

➢ Keep a record of the number of points you score, and attempt to set a new record each time you play the game.

LINE IT UP

➢ If competing with multiple players, the winner is the player with the most points, once all players have had an equal number of turns.

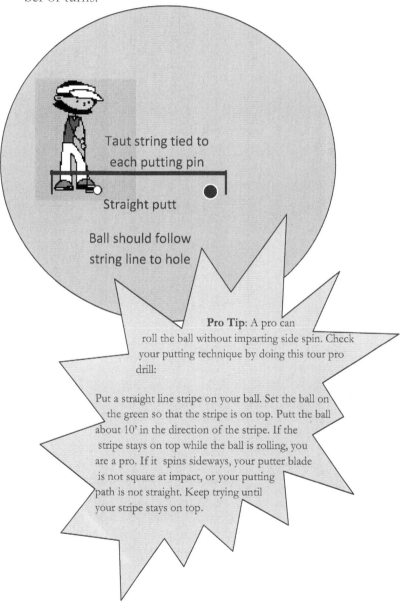

Taut string tied to each putting pin

Straight putt

Ball should follow string line to hole

Pro Tip: A pro can roll the ball without imparting side spin. Check your putting technique by doing this tour pro drill:

Put a straight line stripe on your ball. Set the ball on the green so that the stripe is on top. Putt the ball about 10' in the direction of the stripe. If the stripe stays on top while the ball is rolling, you are a pro. If it spins sideways, your putter blade is not square at impact, or your putting path is not straight. Keep trying until your stripe stays on top.

LINE IT UP

Date	Estimated Distance From Hole	Number of Putts In A Row

LINE IT UP

Date	Estimated Distance From Hole	Number of Putts In A Row

SCHOOL

School is a ladder putting drill that helps develop distance control. The object is to roll the ball either into the hole or so that it stops within a close distance just past he hole. If successful, you "graduate" to the next grade and try again from farther away.

Equipment Required:

- ✓ 5 or more ball markers (either coins or tees work well)
- ✓ 3-foot ParZone ring

Setup: Please refer to the drawing on the facing page.

➢ Create a "passing zone" by placing the 3-foot ParZone ring around the hole as shown. The passing zone begins at the hole and includes the area within the ParZone target ring.

➢ Beginning a short distance from the hole, place the ball markers at 3-foot increments moving away from the hole. Use your judgment on the spacing of the markers. For beginners, keep the markers closer together. For advanced players, spread them farther apart.

➢ The closest marker represents "1st grade", the next marker "2nd grade", then "3rd grade", and so on.

How To Play:

➢ Beginning at "1st grade," putt toward the hole.

➢ If the ball is holed or finishes inside the "passing zone" the player advances to the next grade and putts again.

SCHOOL

> ➤ If the ball does not finish either in the hole or within the passing zone, the player goes back to 1st grade.

> ➤ If it becomes too easy to reach the highest grade, spread the grade markers farther apart or use a breaking putt.

> ➤ If playing individually, keep a record of the number of putts you require to reach the highest grade and attempt to set a new (lower) record each time you play.

> ➤ If competing with multiple players, the winner is the only player to reach the highest grade, once all players have had an equal number of turns (i.e., when a player reaches the end, any remaining players after him in the round get a chance to tie). In the event of a tie, continue adding grades farther from the hole until only one person passes.

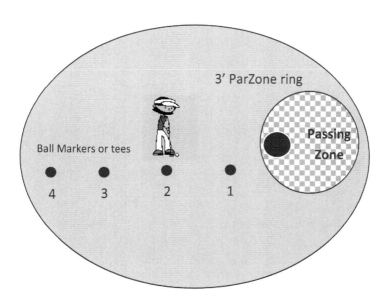

SCHOOL

Date	Grade Reached (circle one)	# Putts Required to Reach Final Grade
	1 2 3 4 5 6 7 8 9	
	1 2 3 4 5 6 7 8 9	
	1 2 3 4 5 6 7 8 9	
	1 2 3 4 5 6 7 8 9	
	1 2 3 4 5 6 7 8 9	
	1 2 3 4 5 6 7 8 9	
	1 2 3 4 5 6 7 8 9	
	1 2 3 4 5 6 7 8 9	
	1 2 3 4 5 6 7 8 9	
	1 2 3 4 5 6 7 8 9	
	1 2 3 4 5 6 7 8 9	
	1 2 3 4 5 6 7 8 9	
	1 2 3 4 5 6 7 8 9	
	1 2 3 4 5 6 7 8 9	

SCHOOL

Date	Grade Reached (circle one)	# Putts Required to Reach Final Grade
	1 2 3 4 5 6 7 8 9	
	1 2 3 4 5 6 7 8 9	
	1 2 3 4 5 6 7 8 9	
	1 2 3 4 5 6 7 8 9	
	1 2 3 4 5 6 7 8 9	
	1 2 3 4 5 6 7 8 9	
	1 2 3 4 5 6 7 8 9	
	1 2 3 4 5 6 7 8 9	
	1 2 3 4 5 6 7 8 9	
	1 2 3 4 5 6 7 8 9	
	1 2 3 4 5 6 7 8 9	
	1 2 3 4 5 6 7 8 9	
	1 2 3 4 5 6 7 8 9	
	1 2 3 4 5 6 7 8 9	

SEQUENCE

Sequence tests your ability to repeatedly hit good shots with any club, and helps develop consistent shotmaking technique and performance under pressure.

Equipment Required:

- ✓ Supply of golf balls (either regular balls or range balls)
- ✓ ParZone ring (size determined by skill level)
- ✓ 2 ball markers or tees

Setup: Please refer to the drawing on the facing page.

➢ Create a starting point by placing 2 ball markers or tees 6 feet apart either on the green (for putting) or in an area suitable for chipping, pitching or bunker shots of any length. Many setups are possible, depending on whether you are playing the game while putting, chipping, pitching, bunker, or full shots.

➢ Depending on whether you are playing Sequence with putting, chipping, pitching, bunker, or full shots, you must create a target goal. This could be the hole, any size ring, or a even a practice green, depending upon your personal standard of an acceptable shot. The goal should be set so that it is challenging, but still reasonably achievable.

How To Play:

➢ The object of the game is to hit as many consecutive balls into your target as possible.

➢ Define your goal for the situation. For shorter putts, it might be the hole. For longer putts, it may be to putt the ball into the 3' ParZone ring. For chip, pitch, or standard bunker shots,

SEQUENCE

it may be to stop the ball within the 6' ParZone ring. For difficult bunker shots, it may be to stop the ball on the green.

➤ Begin hitting shots toward your goal. If you succeed (as defined above), continue until you fail to achieve your goal.

➤ Each ball that scores a goal counts as one point. The game (or your turn) ends when you fail to score a goal.

➤ Keep a record of the number of points you score, and attempt to set a new record each time you play the game.

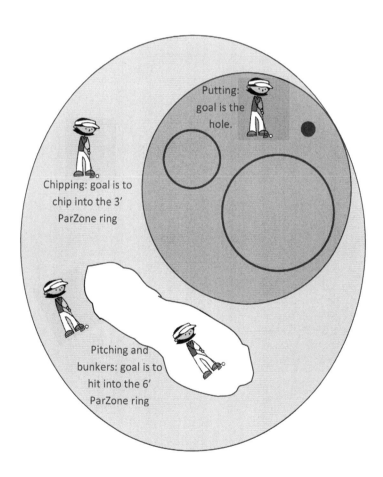

SEQUENCE

Date	Subject (circle one)	Goal (circle one)		No. of Points
	Putt Chip Pitch Bunker Full	In Hole	Ring 3' 6'	On Green
	Putt Chip Pitch Bunker Full	In Hole	Ring 3' 6'	On Green
	Putt Chip Pitch Bunker Full	In Hole	Ring 3' 6'	On Green
	Putt Chip Pitch Bunker Full	In Hole	Ring 3' 6'	On Green
	Putt Chip Pitch Bunker Full	In Hole	Ring 3' 6'	On Green
	Putt Chip Pitch Bunker Full	In Hole	Ring 3' 6'	On Green
	Putt Chip Pitch Bunker Full	In Hole	Ring 3' 6'	On Green
	Putt Chip Pitch Bunker Full	In Hole	Ring 3' 6'	On Green
	Putt Chip Pitch Bunker Full	In Hole	Ring 3' 6'	On Green
	Putt Chip Pitch Bunker Full	In Hole	Ring 3' 6'	On Green
	Putt Chip Pitch Bunker Full	In Hole	Ring 3' 6'	On Green
	Putt Chip Pitch Bunker Full	In Hole	Ring 3' 6'	On Green

SEQUENCE

Date	Subject (circle one)	Goal (circle one)		No. of Points
	Putt Chip Pitch Bunker Full	In Ring On	Hole 3' 6' Green	
	Putt Chip Pitch Bunker Full	In Ring On	Hole 3' 6' Green	
	Putt Chip Pitch Bunker Full	In Ring On	Hole 3' 6' Green	
	Putt Chip Pitch Bunker Full	In Ring On	Hole 3' 6' Green	
	Putt Chip Pitch Bunker Full	In Ring On	Hole 3' 6' Green	
	Putt Chip Pitch Bunker Full	In Ring On	Hole 3' 6' Green	
	Putt Chip Pitch Bunker Full	In Ring On	Hole 3' 6' Green	
	Putt Chip Pitch Bunker Full	In Ring On	Hole 3' 6' Green	
	Putt Chip Pitch Bunker Full	In Ring On	Hole 3' 6' Green	
	Putt Chip Pitch Bunker Full	In Ring On	Hole 3' 6' Green	
	Putt Chip Pitch Bunker Full	In Ring On	Hole 3' 6' Green	
	Putt Chip Pitch Bunker Full	In Ring On	Hole 3' 6' Green	

SNEAK ATTACK

Sneak Attack is the opposite of "Catch Me (If You Can)," and helps develop distance control and feel for all types of shots, including putting, chipping, pitching, bunkers, and even full shots. The object is simple: hit each ball as close as possible to the prior ball without going past – in other words, "sneak up" on the prior ball..

Equipment Required:

- ✓ Supply of golf balls (either regular balls or range balls)
- ✓ 2 ball markers or tees

Setup: Please refer to the drawing on the facing page.

- ➢ Create a starting point by placing 2 ball markers or tees 6 feet apart either on the green (for putting) or in an area suitable for chipping, pitching, bunkers or full shots.

- ➢ Create an out-of-bounds limit or maximum distance that the first ball can travel. For putting, this could be the edge of the green, a string stretched across the green, or some other area. For chipping, pitching, and bunkers, this could be a line about 25 yards away from the starting point. For full shots it could be a yardage marker.

How To Play:

- ➢ The goal is to hit as many balls in a row as possible where no ball travels farther than the prior ball ("target ball"). Each ball must "sneak up" on the target ball.

- ➢ Begin by hitting the first ball as far as possible, without going over the out-of-bounds limit. That ball becomes the target ball for the next shot.

SNEAK ATTACK

➤ Hit each subsequent ball, trying to come as close as possible to the prior ball. Each ball that stops short of the prior ball scores a point and that ball becomes the new target ball for the next shot.

➤ If a ball touches or goes farther than the target ball, the game ends.

➤ Continue hitting until a ball either touches the target ball or goes farther than the target ball. Score a point each time the ball stops short of the target ball.

➤ If playing individually, keep a record of the number of points you score, and attempt to set a new record each time you play the game.

➤ If competing with multiple players, the winner is the player with the most points, once all players have had an equal number of turns.

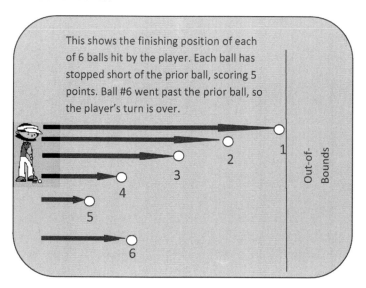

This shows the finishing position of each of 6 balls hit by the player. Each ball has stopped short of the prior ball, scoring 5 points. Ball #6 went past the prior ball, so the player's turn is over.

SNEAK ATTACK

Date	Subject (circle one)	Boundary Limit Distance	Number of Points
	Putt-Chip-Pitch-Bunker		
	Putt-Chip-Pitch-Bunker		
	Putt-Chip-Pitch-Bunker		
	Putt-Chip-Pitch-Bunker		
	Putt-Chip-Pitch-Bunker		
	Putt-Chip-Pitch-Bunker		
	Putt-Chip-Pitch-Bunker		
	Putt-Chip-Pitch-Bunker		
	Putt-Chip-Pitch-Bunker		
	Putt-Chip-Pitch-Bunker		
	Putt-Chip-Pitch-Bunker		
	Putt-Chip-Pitch-Bunker		
	Putt-Chip-Pitch-Bunker		
	Putt-Chip-Pitch-Bunker		

SNEAK ATTACK

Date	Subject (circle one)	Boundary Limit Distance	Number of Points
	Putt-Chip-Pitch-Bunker		
	Putt-Chip-Pitch-Bunker		
	Putt-Chip-Pitch-Bunker		
	Putt-Chip-Pitch-Bunker		
	Putt-Chip-Pitch-Bunker		
	Putt-Chip-Pitch-Bunker		
	Putt-Chip-Pitch-Bunker		
	Putt-Chip-Pitch-Bunker		
	Putt-Chip-Pitch-Bunker		
	Putt-Chip-Pitch-Bunker		
	Putt-Chip-Pitch-Bunker		
	Putt-Chip-Pitch-Bunker		
	Putt-Chip-Pitch-Bunker		
	Putt-Chip-Pitch-Bunker		

WICKET TRAIL

Wicket Trail helps visualize breaks, or slopes, on the green and helps understand how putts break. The object is to arrange wickets on the green so that you can putt through them to the hole.

Equipment Required:

- ✓ 5 ParKit Golf Wickets (large 1 point wickets)
- ✓ 2 ball markers

Setup: Please refer to the drawing on the facing page.

➤ Choose a spot on the practice putting green with some slope that will produce a breaking putt.

➤ Place the two ball markers about 6" apart on the green, about 10 feet away from the hole. Place your ball between the markers.

➤ Survey the putt and estimate the curvature of the putt. Mark your expected putting line by inserting each wicket into the putting green. Arrange the wickets in a curved line representing the line you think your ball must follow to reach the hole.

How To Play:

➤ The object of the game is to putt your ball through all five wickets and into the hole in the least number of tries.

➤ Begin by putting from between the ball markers toward the first wicket with enough speed to reach the hole.

➤ If your ball goes through each wicket and into the hole, the game is over. If the ball does not go through each wicket, try the putt again, and reset the wickets as needed. Use your best judgment of the line of the putt to reset only those wickets

WICKET TRAIL

that need to be moved in order to mark the line of the putt to the hole.

➢ If the game seems too easy, start farther from the hole or select a putt across a more severe slope.

➢ Keep a record of the number of tries you require to make the putt while passing through each wicket, and attempt to set a new record each time you play the game.

➢ If competing with multiple players, the winner is the first player to hole the putt while passing through each wicket.

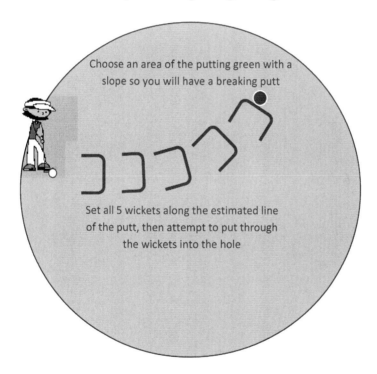

Choose an area of the putting green with a slope so you will have a breaking putt

Set all 5 wickets along the estimated line of the putt, then attempt to put through the wickets into the hole

WICKET TRAIL

Date	Estimated Distance From Hole	Number of Tries Before Holing Putt

WICKET TRAIL

Date	Estimated Distance From Hole	Number of Tries Before Holing Putt

NOTES

NOTES

NOTES

ABOUT THE AUTHORS

Rick Heard is a PGA teaching professional and co-owner of the Don Law Golf Academy in Boca Raton, Florida. A PGA member since 2002, Rick was president of the Southeast Chapter of the South Florida Section PGA for six years ending in 2012, and was awarded the chapter's Golf Professional of the Year award for 2010. Rick also received the 2002 chapter Junior Golf Leader award and the Southeast Chapter PGA Horton Smith education award for both 2007 and 2008.

Don Law has been a PGA member since 1993 and a teaching professional and director of instruction since 1995. A highly decorated professional, Don was awarded the 2012 National Junior Golf Leader of the Year award by the PGA of America. Don has received 14 PGA chapter and section awards, including the 2011 Golf Professional of the Year in the South Florida PGA Section. He is also a US Kids Master Instructor.

The Don Law Golf Academy specializes in teaching juniors, and has hundreds of young golfers in its classes and camps in four South Florida locations. The DLGA also has a full suite of expert instructional programs for adults of all abilities.

Don and Rick are co-founders and partners with Diana Law, Bill Scott, and Chad Kurmel in ParKit Golf, which creates innovative teaching tools and materials to make junior golf classes and camps both fun and educational.

Printed in Great Britain
by Amazon.co.uk, Ltd.,
Marston Gate.